FOCUS ON THE FAMILY® PRESENTS

The Family project™
A Divine Reflection

RECOVER. RENEW. RECLAIM.

PARTICIPANT'S GUIDE

The Family project™

A Divine Reflection

RECOVER. RENEW. RECLAIM.

CONTENTS

CONTENTS

PROLOGUE

WELCOME TO THE FAMILY PROJECT CURRICULUM!

Thank you for investing the time and effort to learn more about God's design for the family and how it reflects His very own nature.

As we will see in session 1 of this curriculum, as we explore the meaning of family, we're also embarking on a journey to answer three key questions that all human beings ask in some form:

Where do we come from?

What are we?

Where are we going?

In this pursuit, we will encounter two primary reference points to help us find answers. ▶

Just as every town has main roads that serve as the common reference points for getting around, so also there are two main "intersecting roads" in our journey.

OUR EAST-WEST PATHWAY: FULLER WORLDVIEW BOULEVARD

The Christian worldview is typically understood in three parts:

Creation
Fall
Redemption

But in looking at the big picture, we see there are really four additional parts, with the other parts in the smaller arrows below:

PRE-CREATION ▷ CREATION ▷ FALL ▷ INCARNATI[ON]

As we move through each session, the significance of each will be made clear.

OUR NORTH-SOUTH PATHWAY: DEFINITIVE STATEMENT AVENUE

This second main thoroughfare consists of four definitive statements from God that give meaning and understanding to where we come from, what we are, and where we're going:

1 God's First Definitive Statement: "Let us make man in our image..." (Genesis 1:26).

2 God's Second Definitive Statement: "It is not good that the man should be alone..." (Genesis 2:18).

3 God's Third Definitive Statement: "Behold, the man has become like one of us..." (Genesis 3:22).

4 God's Fourth Definitive Statement: "Behold, I am making all things new" (Revelation 21:5).

Look for these worldview parts and definitive statements as they address those three key human questions in order through the sessions that follow.

REDEMPTION → ASCENSION → CONSUMMATION

For more resources on Christian worldview and God's plan for the family, please visit **familyproject.com**.

YOU ARE HERE

AN INTRODUCTION TO
THE FAMILY

INTRODUCTION

In the words of an old pop tune, we are all by nature "people who need people." We need to belong to others, and we long for a meaningful role—an assignment or task— within that community. Without belonging and significance, life seems to have no purpose. But how did we come to be such creatures? The book of Genesis tells all.

NOTES

Watch the DVD and record your thoughts here.

Let's turn to the ultimate authority, the Bible, for our starting point. Read individually or as a group:

THE **BACKSTORY**

Then the Lord God formed the man of dust from the ground and breathed into his nostrils the breath of life, and the man became a living creature. And the Lord God planted a garden in Eden, in the east, and there he put the man whom he had formed. . . . The Lord God took the man and put him in the garden of Eden to work it and keep it. . . . Now out of the ground the Lord God had formed every beast of the field and every bird of the heavens and brought them to the man to see what he would call them. And whatever the man called every living creature, that was its name. The man gave names to all livestock and to the birds of the heavens and to every beast of the field. But for Adam there was not found a helper fit for him.

—Genesis 2:7-8, 15, 19-20

You might also want to read:
Ecclesiastes 4:9-12.

Use the blank lines below the discussion questions to record your initial thoughts, questions, and whatever God might be saying to you through the video, so you can review and reflect on all of this later.

WHAT DO YOU
THINK?

1. According to Genesis, how did God give mankind a place of significance right from the beginning of time? Despite this role, what was missing?

_____

_____

_____

_____

_____

_____

2. What would it be like to grow up without love and acceptance? Can you tell us about someone you know who had that experience? What happens to us when we don't feel we belong to anyone?

_____

_____

_____

_____

_____

_____

3. Why do we all need to feel significant? What are some things you've observed people doing to achieve that? How do *you* strive to be important?

_____

_____

_____

_____

_____

4. What does the fact that God gave us these needs for belonging and significance tell us about Him? About ourselves?

_____

_____

_____

_____

_____

5. Does being in a family help you feel significant? If so, how? Tell us about a time when you or your family did something that helped a member feel a real sense of belonging and significance.

_____

_____

_____

_____

_____

ONE
STEP
I CAN TAKE
TOMORROW

Think of and write down at least one practical thing you can do tomorrow as a result of today's session.

_____

_____

_____

_____

_____

_____

_____

_____

_____

_____

_____

_____

_____

_____

_____

_____

_____

_____

WRAP-UP

Today we reflected on the fact that we each derive our identity from whatever purpose shapes our life and the community or family of which we're a part. Understanding God's design of the family is vital to our becoming good spouses, parents, and children. Thus equipped, a strong family can be used by God to strengthen the church and be a powerful witness in the world.

Remember that for more resources on Christian worldview and God's plan for the family, you can visit **familyproject.com**.

LET US MAKE MAN
(IMAGO DEI)

GOD CREATED MANKIND IN HIS OWN IMAGE.

INTRODUCTION

What's so special about mankind? A lot of people today would say, "Absolutely nothing!" In their view, the earth itself and the animals that crawl on it are more important than man, who has messed everything up. But who is man? In Psalm 8, David pondered that question because he saw both our seeming insignificance and yet our astounding nature that sets us apart from all the rest of creation.

NOTES

Watch the DVD and record your thoughts here.

Let's turn to the ultimate authority, the Bible, for our starting point. Read individually or as a group:

THE BACKSTORY

Then God said, "Let us make man in our image, after our likeness. And let them have dominion over the fish of the sea and over the birds of the heavens and over the livestock and over all the earth and over every creeping thing that creeps on the earth."

—Genesis 1:26

When I look at your heavens, the work of your fingers, the moon and the stars, which you have set in place, what is man that you are mindful of him, and the son of man that you care for him? Yet you have made him a little lower than the heavenly beings and crowned him with glory and honor.

—Psalm 8:3-5

You might also want to read:
Matthew 25:37-40
Romans 1:19-20
2 Corinthians 3:18
Colossians 3:9-10

Use the blank lines below the discussion questions to record your initial thoughts, questions, and whatever God might be saying to you through the video, so you can review and reflect on all of this later.

WHAT DO YOU THINK?

1. How does this session answer those key human questions of where we come from and what we are?

_____

_____

_____

_____

_____

_____

2. What does it mean that we're made in the image of God? In what ways are we like Him? In what ways are we different?

_____

_____

_____

_____

_____

_____

_____

3. How does being formed in His image affect the way you think and feel about yourself? About others? Explain how this gives meaning and significance to your life.

4. From your observations, how do people pervert the image of God in the ways they think and act?

5. Describe something you did or said this past week that likely reflected God's own nature. In another moment, how did your behavior or attitude fail to mirror the Lord? What areas do you need to work on so that you can more clearly reflect the image of God?

ONE
STEP
I CAN TAKE
TOMORROW

Think of and write down at least one practical thing you can do tomorrow as a result of today's session.

_____

_____

_____

_____

_____

_____

_____

_____

_____

_____

_____

_____

_____

_____

_____

_____

WRAP-UP

D id anyone ever say to you as a child, "My, you're the spitting image of your father"? Or, instead, "Shame on you; your mother would never have acted that way"? We bear a tremendous responsibility, because the person we should remind people of is God himself. But we can do that only if we see others as people made in the image of God, deserving the kind of attention and compassion that He wants them to receive through us.

IT IS NOT GOOD TO BE ALONE:
HOW FAMILY COMPLETES
THE IMAGO DEI

SESSION

3

*LONELINESS AND
GOD'S ANTIDOTE*

INTRODUCTION

Every time God created something, "He saw that it was good"—with one exception. "It is *not* good," He said, "that the man should be alone" (Genesis 1:18, emphasis added). So He created Eve, and the rest is, literally, history. But there are still lonely people. Let's think about that today.

NOTES

Watch the DVD and record your thoughts here.

Let's turn to the ultimate
authority, the Bible, for
our starting point. Read
individually or as a group:

THE **BACKSTORY**

Then the Lord God said, "It is not good that the man should be alone; I will make him a helper fit for him." . . . So the Lord God caused a deep sleep to fall upon the man, and while he slept took one of his ribs and closed up its place with flesh. And the rib that the Lord God had taken from the man he made into a woman and brought her to the man. Then the man said, "This at last is bone of my bones and flesh of my flesh; she shall be called Woman, because she was taken out of Man." Therefore a man shall leave his father and his mother and hold fast to his wife, and they shall become one flesh.

—Genesis 2:18, 21-24

"I do not ask for these only, but also for those who will believe in me through their word, that they may all be one, just as you, Father, are in me, and I in you, that they also may be in us, so that the world may believe that you have sent me. The glory that you have given me I have given to them, that they may be one even as we are one, I in them and you in me, that they may become perfectly one, so that the world may know that you sent me and loved them even as you loved me. Father, I desire that they also, whom you have given me, may be with me where I am, to see my glory that you have given me because you loved me before the foundation of the world. O righteous Father, even though the world does not know you, I know you, and these know that you have sent me. I made known to them your name, and I will continue to make it known, that the love with which you have loved me may be in them, and I in them."

—John 17:20-26

You might also want to read:
Proverbs 18:22; 19:14; Ephesians 5:31-33; Matthew 3:13-17.

Use the blank lines below the discussion questions to record your initial thoughts, questions, and whatever God might be saying to you through the video, so you can review and reflect on all of this later.

WHAT DO YOU THINK?

1. Why did God make us so that we cannot live without having others to relate to? What's wrong with the idea of a solitary man or woman?

_____

_____

_____

_____

_____

2. When have you felt the loneliest? Describe some of those times. What causes loneliness, often even for those who have plenty of casual friends, acquaintances, and family members?

_____

_____

_____

_____

_____

3. Give an instance of how marriage uniquely meets the need for human connection. How is it different from our friendships? From sibling relationships? If you're married, in what way is your spouse a "helper" fit for you?

_____

_____

_____

4. In what ways do all families reflect the nature of God? If you're married (or in marriages you've observed), do your marriage and family life have the same flavor, or same beauty, that you sensed from the John 17 reading? Why or why not? What experience comes to mind?

_____

_____

_____

5. This session's video shows the painting of the Creation on the ceiling of the Sistine Chapel in Rome. God is pictured reaching out to Adam but holding Eve in His arm. What might the painter have been thinking about God's feelings for men and women?

_____

_____

_____

6. How should the fact that the family reflects God's nature influence the way we live together day-to-day?

_____

_____

_____

_____

ONE
STEP
I CAN TAKE
TOMORROW

Think of and write down at least one practical thing you can do tomorrow as a result of today's session.

WRAP-UP

When God saw that Adam was alone, He didn't bring him some buddies to hang out with. Instead, He created a whole different kind of human being and named her Eve. So in a profound way, the ultimate answer to loneliness is the companionship of someone of the opposite sex—specifically, someone with whom a man or woman can form an intimate, unbreakable bond. And out of that bond, the two create a family, which itself is an image of God.

FOR THIS
REASON

*MARRIAGE AND
SEXUALITY ARE
GOD'S IDEA.*

INTRODUCTION

It's trendy these days to think that men and women are basically the same kind of people inside, and that marriage is whatever we want it to be, however we want to define it. That's why we need to go back to Scripture. There we discover where male and female originated, and we see where marriage came from in the beginning.

NOTES

Watch the DVD and record your thoughts here.

Let's turn to the ultimate authority, the Bible, for our starting point. Read individually or as a group:

THE **BACKSTORY**

So God created man in his own image, in the image of God he created him; male and female he created them. And God blessed them. And God said to them, "Be fruitful and multiply and fill the earth and subdue it, and have dominion over the fish of the sea and over the birds of the heavens and over every living thing that moves on the earth."

—Genesis 1:27-28

And the rib that the Lord God had taken from the man he made into a woman and brought her to the man. Then the man said, "This at last is bone of my bones and flesh of my flesh; she shall be called Woman, because she was taken out of Man." Therefore a man shall leave his father and his mother and hold fast to his wife, and they shall become one flesh.

—Genesis 2:22-24

Let marriage be held in honor among all, and let the marriage bed be undefiled, for God will judge the sexually immoral and adulterous.

—Hebrews 13:4

You might also want to read:
1 Corinthians 7:1-5.

Use the blank lines below the discussion questions to record your initial thoughts, questions, and whatever God might be saying to you through the video, so you can review and reflect on all of this later.

WHAT DO YOU
THINK?

1. What does the fact that God told Adam and Eve, *before* they sinned, to "be fruitful and multiply" tell us about marital intimacy? What good purposes does it serve?

_____

_____

_____

_____

_____

_____

2. If you're married, why? Did you get married just because it was the accepted thing to do? Or to alleviate loneliness? To find happiness or sexual satisfaction? To have a family? What is the fundamental reason for marriage?

_____

_____

_____

_____

_____

3. Is sex ever a physical act only, with no emotional or spiritual dimension? Why or why not?

_____

_____

_____

_____

_____

4. In everyday practice, how do you and your spouse include God as the third party in your marriage?

_____

_____

_____

_____

_____

5. What has marriage done for your character, your spiritual maturity? Can you describe an incident that helped you grow?

_____

_____

_____

_____

_____

_____

ONE STEP
I CAN TAKE
TOMORROW

Think of and write down at least one practical thing you can do tomorrow as a result of today's session.

_____

_____

_____

_____

_____

_____

_____

_____

_____

_____

_____

_____

_____

_____

_____

_____

WRAP-UP

Since marriage and sexuality are among God's best inventions, it shouldn't surprise us that they have been greatly affected by the coming of sin into the world. In the next session, we'll take a closer look at what has happened since the Fall.

THE MAN HAS NOW BECOME LIKE ONE OF US

THE UNDOING OF FAMILY

INTRODUCTION

It's the saddest story in history—how Adam and Eve's happy marriage self-destructed after disobeying God, thereby threatening every family that followed. But it's important to review the events in the Garden of Eden, because the story tells us exactly what we're up against when we try to succeed at building a family.

NOTES

Watch the DVD and record your thoughts here.

Let's turn to the ultimate authority, the Bible, for our starting point. Read individually or as a group:

THE **BACKSTORY**

Now the serpent was more crafty than any other beast of the field that the Lord God had made. He said to the woman, "Did God actually say, 'You shall not eat of any tree in the garden'?" And the woman said to the serpent, "We may eat of the fruit of the trees in the garden, but God said, 'You shall not eat of the fruit of the tree that is in the midst of the garden, neither shall you touch it, lest you die. '" But the serpent said to the woman, "You will not surely die. For God knows that when you eat of it your eyes will be opened, and you will be like God, knowing good and evil." So when the woman saw that the tree was good for food, and that it was a delight to the eyes, and that the tree was to be desired to make one wise, she took of its fruit and ate, and she also gave some to her husband who was with her, and he ate. Then the eyes of both were opened, and they knew that they were naked. And they sewed fig leaves together and made themselves loincloths. And they heard the sound of the Lord God walking in the garden in the cool of the day, and the man and his wife hid themselves from the presence of the Lord God among the trees of the garden. But the Lord God called to the man and said to him, "Where are you?" And he said, "I heard the sound of you in the garden, and I was afraid, because I was naked, and I hid myself." He said, "Who told you that you were naked? Have you eaten of the tree of which I commanded you not to eat?" The man said, "The woman whom you gave to be with me, she gave me fruit of the tree, and I ate." Then the Lord God said to the woman, "What is this that you have done?" The woman said, "The serpent deceived me, and I ate." . . . Then the Lord God said, "Behold, the man has become like one of us in knowing good and evil."

—Genesis 3:1-13, 22

You might also want to read:
Romans 5:12-15; 1 Corinthians 15:22, 45-49.

Use the blank lines below the discussion questions to record your initial thoughts, questions, and whatever God might be saying to you through the video, so you can review and reflect on all of this later.

WHAT DO YOU
THINK?

1. Why do you think the serpent first approached just one person, Eve, rather than the couple? How did this evil tactic help break up their relationship?

_____

_____

_____

_____

_____

_____

2. In what ways did Adam and Eve die when they ate the forbidden fruit?

_____

_____

_____

_____

_____

_____

3. Satan is enraged not just with God, but also with marriage and family, since they are a representation of God. How did Adam and Eve's sin affect their marriage? How has it affected every marriage since? Do you have an anecdote to share from your own marriage?

_____

_____

_____

_____

_____

4. Just as the Fall attacked the family, so also salvation came through a family. How does Jesus's birth into a family, and the fact that He remained in a family to the end of His earthly life, help you relate to Him? Do you see Him as fully human, or do you tend to think mostly of His divinity? Why?

_____

_____

_____

_____

_____

5. How does God use family to help bring good out of the Fall?

_____

_____

_____

ONE STEP
I CAN TAKE TOMORROW

Think of and write down at least one practical thing you can do tomorrow as a result of today's session.

WRAP-UP

By one man, Adam, came sin and death. By another man, Jesus, came redemption and life. Every day, we experience both of those realities in our marriage and family life. But we can be victorious if we at least stay together as a family. Sadly, many marriages don't hold together long enough to work through the problems. We'll look at that in our next session.

WHAT GOD HAS
JOINED
TOGETHER

*A BREAKUP THAT
HURTS EVERYONE,
INCLUDING GOD*

INTRODUCTION

Everyone has an opinion about when divorce is justified or not. Sometimes even Christians seem reluctant to consult Scripture regarding the issue of divorce and remarriage. But only one thing matters: what Jesus said about marriage and divorce. So we begin this session by listening to His words.

NOTES

Watch the DVD and record your thoughts here.

Let's turn to the ultimate authority, the Bible, for our starting point. Read individually or as a group:

THE **BACKSTORY**

And Pharisees came up and in order to test him asked, "Is it lawful for a man to divorce his wife?" He answered them, "What did Moses command you?" They said, "Moses allowed a man to write a certificate of divorce and to send her away." And Jesus said to them, "Because of your hardness of heart he wrote you this commandment. But from the beginning of creation, 'God made them male and female. ' 'Therefore a man shall leave his father and mother and hold fast to his wife, and the two shall become one flesh. ' So they are no longer two but one flesh. What therefore God has joined together, let not man separate."

—Mark 10:2-9

You might also want to read:
Luke 16:18
1 Corinthians 7:10

Use the blank lines below the discussion questions to record your initial thoughts, questions, and whatever God might be saying to you through the video, so you can review and reflect on all of this later.

WHAT DO YOU
THINK?

1. Why is the family structure of father, mother, and children the norm in cultures around the world? Why have alternative forms of family never really had staying power?

_____

_____

_____

_____

_____

_____

2. In what ways are healthy families beneficial for those who are part of them? For society as a whole?

_____

_____

_____

_____

_____

_____

3. What happens to society when a large number of families fall apart? Share a story or two of how this disintegration has affected your own family, friends, or community.

_____

_____

_____

_____

4. How does divorce in Christian homes affect what the world thinks of God?

_____

_____

_____

5. How should we view modern efforts to redefine the family, or to have children be "owned by everyone"—that is, controlled by the state rather than by the parents? Tell about any struggle you've faced or freedoms you feel are threatened as a result.

_____

_____

_____

6. How can parents in the church support one another in the task of parenting well?

_____

_____

_____

ONE STEP
I CAN TAKE
TOMORROW

Think of and write down at least one practical thing you can do tomorrow as a result of today's session.

WRAP-UP

Breaking up is *not* hard to do; it's staying together that's a challenge. But doing so is vital, because every child needs and deserves both a mom and a dad, because a father is no substitute for a mother, and vice versa. Next session, we'll explore what's unique about mothers.

MOTHERS
AS IMAGE-BEARERS

*THERE'S NO ONE
LIKE MOM—
EXCEPT GOD.*

INTRODUCTION

Once upon a time, a teenage girl from a small town in Galilee let God have His way in her life, and as a result she became the most famous mother in all of history. Mary, the "mother of all mothers" and the mother of Jesus, provides a fitting introduction to our topic in this session, motherhood.

NOTES

Watch the DVD and record your thoughts here.

Let's turn to the ultimate authority, the Bible, for our starting point. Read individually or as a group:

And the angel said to her, "Do not be afraid, Mary, for you have found favor with God. And behold, you will conceive in your womb and bear a son, and you shall call his name Jesus." . . . And Mary said, "Behold, I am the servant of the Lord; let it be to me according to your word." . . . And when Elizabeth heard the greeting of Mary, the baby leaped in her womb. And Elizabeth was filled with the Holy Spirit, and she exclaimed with a loud cry, "Blessed are you among women, and blessed is the fruit of your womb! And why is this granted to me that the mother of my Lord should come to me?" . . . And Mary said, "My soul magnifies the Lord, and my spirit rejoices in God my Savior, for he has looked on the humble estate of his servant. For behold, from now on all generations will call me blessed."

—Luke 1:30-31, 38, 41-43, 46-48

When Jesus [on the cross] saw his mother and the disciple whom he loved standing nearby, he said to his mother, "Woman, behold, your son!" Then he said to the disciple, "Behold, your mother!" And from that hour the disciple took her to his own home.

—John 19:26-27

You might also want to read:
John 2:1-11.

Use the blank lines below the discussion questions to record your initial thoughts, questions, and whatever God might be saying to you through the video, so you can review and reflect on all of this later.

WHAT DO YOU THINK?

1. How did Jesus view and treat His own mother? What was admirable about Mary's character? To put it another way, why do you think God chose her, above all women, to be the mother of our Savior?

_____

_____

_____

_____

_____

_____

2. In what ways is God like a mother to us? How should God's "mothering" nature serve as a model for human mothers? What's unique about a mother's role in the family?

_____

_____

_____

_____

_____

3. How would you describe the ideal mother? Who in your life
   has come closest to that ideal? (Tell us about her.) What do you
   appreciate most about your own mother?

_____

_____

_____

_____

_____

4. Moms, what to you is the most meaningful aspect of motherhood?
   How did becoming a mother affect your relationship to God? What
   has it taught you about Him and His heart toward us, His children?

_____

_____

_____

_____

_____

5. Have you observed or even experienced firsthand an attack on
   motherhood in today's culture? If so, tell us about it. What ideas
   about women form the basis for such attacks?

_____

_____

_____

_____

_____

ONE
STEP
I CAN TAKE
TOMORROW

Think of and write down at least one practical thing you can do tomorrow as a result of today's session.

WRAP-UP

Who else bears the image of God? That would be fathers, since God himself is pleased to bear that title. Next session, we stop to ponder the character of our Father in heaven and the nature of fatherhood today.

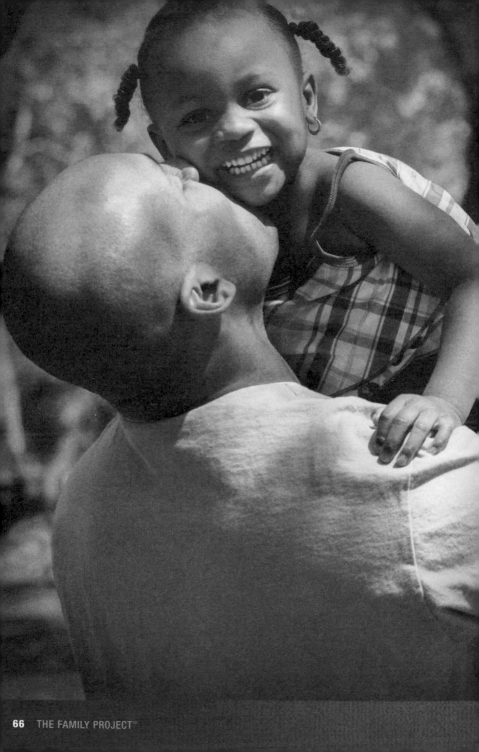

FATHERS
AS IMAGE-BEARERS

"OUR FATHER IN HEAVEN"
SETS THE EXAMPLE.

INTRODUCTION

Jesus had a lot to say about His Father. But since an invisible God can be hard to grasp, Jesus chose to communicate some of His most powerful truths through word pictures—those brief stories we know as parables. In this lesson, as we turn to the topic of fatherhood, we begin with one of the most well known of Jesus's parables.

NOTES

Watch the DVD and record your thoughts here.

Let's turn to the ultimate
authority, the Bible, for
our starting point. Read
individually or as a group:

THE **BACKSTORY**

And he said, "There was a man who had two sons. And the younger of them said to his father, 'Father, give me the share of property that is coming to me. ' And he divided his property between them. Not many days later, the younger son gathered all he had and took a journey into a far country, and there he squandered his property in reckless living. And when he had spent everything, a severe famine arose in that country, and he began to be in need. So he went and hired himself out to one of the citizens of that country, who sent him into his fields to feed pigs. And he was longing to be fed with the pods that the pigs ate, and no one gave him anything.

"But when he came to himself, he said, 'How many of my father's hired servants have more than enough bread, but I perish here with hunger! I will arise and go to my father, and I will say to him, "Father, I have sinned against heaven and before you. I am no longer worthy to be called your son. Treat me as one of your hired servants."' And he arose and came to his father. But while he was still a long way off, his father saw him and felt compassion, and ran and embraced him and kissed him. And the son said to him, 'Father, I have sinned against heaven and before you. I am no longer worthy to be called your son. ' But the father said to his servants, 'Bring quickly the best robe, and put it on him, and put a ring on his hand, and shoes on his feet. And bring the fattened calf and kill it, and let us eat and celebrate. For this my son was dead, and is alive again; he was lost, and is found.'"

—Luke 15:11-24

You might also want to read:
John 3:35; 11:41-42; 15:9-10; Ephesians 3:14-16.

WHAT DO YOU
THINK?

1. The parable we just read is more about the father than about his wayward son. Through this story, what was Jesus saying about God? How might God's "fathering" nature serve as a model for human fathers?

_____

_____

_____

_____

_____

2. No cultures have a problem called "motherlessness," but nearly all have one called "fatherlessness." Given what fatherhood represents, why do you think it is so strongly under attack?

_____

_____

_____

_____

3. What happens to a family when the father doesn't fulfill his role or isn't even there? Any personal experiences you wish to share?

_____

_____

_____

4. How do the media portray fathers today, and what impact has this had on our culture? Which images or examples come to your mind? What other factors or influences have diminished the role of fathers in our society?

_____

_____

_____

5. How would you describe the ideal father? Who in your life has come closest to that ideal? (Tell us about him.) What do you appreciate most about your own dad?

_____

_____

_____

6. Dads, what to you is the most meaningful aspect of fatherhood? What is unique about your role in the home? How did becoming a father affect your relationship to God? What has it taught you about Him and His heart toward us, His children?

_____

_____

_____

ONE STEP
I CAN TAKE TOMORROW

Think of and write down at least one practical thing you can do tomorrow as a result of today's session.

WRAP-UP

Where there are moms and dads, there are (often) children. And the children are what turn a marriage—a couple—into a family. But what is behind God's command to Adam and Eve to "be fruitful and multiply"? Why are children so important? So valued? That's our topic for session 9.

CHILDREN
AS IMAGE-BEARERS

*UNLESS YOU TURN
AND BECOME
LIKE ONE . . .*

INTRODUCTION

Jesus loves the little children. And so do most people. Children are often what make our lives so enriching. But not everyone feels the same way about kids. "What's so great about being a parent? I already have a life of my own," a newly married Christian might say. That's our topic for the day.

NOTES

Watch the DVD and record your thoughts here.

Let's turn to the ultimate authority, the Bible, for our starting point. Read individually or as a group:

THE BACKSTORY

For you formed my inward parts; you knitted me together in my mother's womb. I praise you, for I am fearfully and wonderfully made. Wonderful are your works; my soul knows it very well. My frame was not hidden from you, when I was being made in secret, intricately woven in the depths of the earth. Your eyes saw my unformed substance; in your book were written, every one of them, the days that were formed for me, when as yet there was none of them.

—Psalm 139:13-16

And they were bringing children to him that he might touch them, and the disciples rebuked them. But when Jesus saw it, he was indignant and said to them, "Let the children come to me; do not hinder them, for to such belongs the kingdom of God. Truly, I say to you, whoever does not receive the kingdom of God like a child shall not enter it." And he took them in his arms and blessed them, laying his hands on them.

—Mark 10:13-16

You might also want to read:
1 John 3:1-2.

Use the blank lines below the
discussion questions to record
your initial thoughts, questions,
and whatever God might be
saying to you through the video,
so you can review and reflect
on all of this later.

WHAT DO YOU
THINK?

1. In what ways do children reflect the nature of God? Why all children, not just the "normal" ones? What has delighted you most about your own children (or nephews or nieces)?

_____

_____

_____

_____

_____

_____

2. What does the fact that Jesus came into the world as a baby and went through every stage of childhood say about how God sees and values children?

_____

_____

_____

_____

_____

3. What would society be like (other than destined for extinction) if there were no children?

_____

_____

_____

_____

4. What's the role of children in the family? How has your outlook on life been changed by them? Describe how being a parent has forced you to grow up and put others first.

_____

_____

_____

_____

5. What scared or scares you most about becoming a parent? Explain. Why do many couples today choose not to have children?

_____

_____

_____

_____

6. How are childhood and children themselves being attacked in the world today? How are these attacks on God himself?

_____

_____

_____

_____

ONE STEP
I CAN TAKE
TOMORROW

Think of and write down at least one practical thing you can do tomorrow as a result of today's session.

WRAP-UP

We've already hinted at what might make some people, even Christians, reluctant to have children. Self-sacrifice doesn't come naturally to any of us. But we should explore this more thoroughly. What's the core of the problem faced by families today? We face the hard facts in our next session.

THE ENEMY

WAR WITHOUT AND WITHIN

INTRODUCTION

It's time to look in the mirror. If we're honest, we will come to the same conclusion the apostle Paul did when he wrote, "I do not understand my own actions. For I do not do what I want, but I do the very thing I hate" (Romans 7:15). Today, we're going to confront the worst enemy of the family today.

NOTES

Watch the DVD and record your thoughts here.

Let's turn to the ultimate authority, the Bible, for our starting point. Read individually or as a group:

THE **BACKSTORY**

Walk by the Spirit, and you will not gratify the desires of the flesh. For the desires of the flesh are against the Spirit, and the desires of the Spirit are against the flesh, for these are opposed to each other, to keep you from doing the things you want to do. But if you are led by the Spirit, you are not under the law. Now the works of the flesh are evident: sexual immorality, impurity, sensuality, idolatry, sorcery, enmity, strife, jealousy, fits of anger, rivalries, dissensions, divisions, envy, drunkenness, orgies, and things like these. I warn you, as I warned you before, that those who do such things will not inherit the kingdom of God. But the fruit of the Spirit is love, joy, peace, patience, kindness, goodness, faithfulness, gentleness, self-control; against such things there is no law. And those who belong to Christ Jesus have crucified the flesh with its passions and desires. If we live by the Spirit, let us also keep in step with the Spirit. Let us not become conceited, provoking one another, envying one another.

— *Galatians 5:16-26*

For people will be lovers of self, lovers of money, proud, arrogant, abusive, disobedient to their parents, ungrateful, unholy, heartless, unappeasable, slanderous, without self-control, brutal, not loving good, treacherous, reckless, swollen with conceit, lovers of pleasure rather than lovers of God, having the appearance of godliness, but denying its power.

— *2 Timothy 3:2-5*

You might also want to read:
Matthew 16:24-25; Romans 7:15-20; Ephesians 6:10-18; 1 Peter 5:8.

Use the blank lines below the discussion questions to record your initial thoughts, questions, and whatever God might be saying to you through the video, so you can review and reflect on all of this later.

WHAT DO YOU
THINK?

1. The video session says that love of self is the family's greatest enemy. How is that self-centeredness demonstrated in daily life?

_____

_____

_____

_____

_____

_____

2. What happens to a family made up of self-seeking individuals? Any anecdotes you can share from experience or personal observation?

_____

_____

_____

_____

_____

_____

_____

3. How does "the world" encourage individualism and self-centeredness? What are some of the pleasures we are told by our culture to seek after?

_____

_____

_____

_____

4. What's the opposite of self-centeredness? How is self-centeredness contrary to God's nature?

_____

_____

_____

_____

5. How can one unselfish family member influence everyone in the home? Again, any stories to tell?

_____

_____

_____

_____

6. What's behind most divorces, including those involving Christians? Does love keep a marriage together, or does selfless commitment to the marriage keep us growing in love? Explain.

_____

_____

_____

_____

ONE STEP
I CAN TAKE
TOMORROW

Think of and write down at least one practical thing you can do tomorrow as a result of today's session.

WRAP-UP

Once again, as the apostle discovered, there's reason for hope in the battle against our own fallen nature. It lies in getting closer to God, in letting His Spirit dwell in us and take control. But just how intimate does God want to become with us? Next time, we look at what He has planned for the near future.

THE GREAT MYSTERY AND DESTINY

A MARRIAGE MADE IN HEAVEN

INTRODUCTION

In this present age, maintaining or growing relationships is a constant struggle. Friendships falter, many marriages crumble, and all of us have difficulty listening to God or "abiding" in Jesus every day. But it will not always be so. The time is coming when we will enjoy being close to one another (without sin) and breathtakingly close to God—eternally! We begin today by reading about the wedding that's in store for us.

NOTES

Watch the DVD and record your thoughts here.

Let's turn to the ultimate authority, the Bible, for our starting point. Read individually or as a group:

THE **BACKSTORY**

Then I heard what seemed to be the voice of a great multitude, like the roar of many waters and like the sound of mighty peals of thunder, crying out, "Hallelujah! For the Lord our God the Almighty reigns. Let us rejoice and exult and give him the glory, for the marriage of the Lamb has come, and his Bride has made herself ready; it was granted her to clothe herself with fine linen, bright and pure"—for the fine linen is the righteous deeds of the saints. And the angel said to me, "Write this: Blessed are those who are invited to the marriage supper of the Lamb." And he said to me, "These are the true words of God."

—Revelation 19:6-9

"Therefore a man shall leave his father and mother and hold fast to his wife, and the two shall become one flesh." This mystery is profound, and I am saying that it refers to Christ and the church.

—Ephesians 5:31-32

The end of all things is at hand; therefore be self-controlled and sober-minded for the sake of your prayers. Above all, keep loving one another earnestly, since love covers a multitude of sins. . . . Beloved, do not be surprised at the fiery trial when it comes upon you to test you, as though something strange were happening to you. But rejoice insofar as you share Christ's sufferings, that you may also rejoice and be glad when his glory is revealed.

—1 Peter 4:7-8, 12-13

You might also want to read:
Matthew 22:1-4; 2 Corinthians 11:2.

Use the blank lines below the discussion questions to record your initial thoughts, questions, and whatever God might be saying to you through the video, so you can review and reflect on all of this later.

WHAT DO YOU THINK?

1. **In what ways does human marriage reflect the church's present and future relationship with Christ? How does this affect your thoughts or feelings toward marriage?**

_____

_____

_____

_____

_____

2. **What does this "marriage" of Christ and His people say about how close He wants to be to us? By what means are you and your family pursuing such a relationship with Him here and now?**

_____

_____

_____

_____

_____

3. How would you describe our responsibility to join with other believers throughout time and space in preparing the bride for the marriage supper?

_____

_____

_____

_____

_____

4. What are you willing to do to defend your family (and families in general) in an increasingly hostile culture? Tell us what you expect Christians to possibly face in your lifetime. How can you help persecuted brothers and sisters in Christ in other countries?

_____

_____

_____

_____

_____

5. How might Christians' living more intentionally by God's design in their marriages and as parents affect the society around them? Can you share any examples of this, either personally or from families you've observed?

_____

_____

_____

_____

_____

ONE STEP
I CAN TAKE
TOMORROW

Think of and write down at least one practical thing you can do tomorrow as a result of today's session.

WRAP-UP

Good things are coming for the people of God. No wedding or wedding reception you ever attended, including your own, can measure up to that happy day when we will celebrate ultimate victory with Jesus and sit down for an unimaginable feast. In the meantime, we have to stay faithful and endure much hostility on behalf of Christ, which may even affect our own families.

MY IMPERFECT FAMILY

*CARRYING
GOD'S IMAGE
INTO THE WORLD*

INTRODUCTION

So what now? What if our own families seem so messed up that we don't feel ready to deal with anything larger? How can we, in our fallen state, possibly get involved in the battle for God's kingdom, which includes defending the family in our community and nation? Scripture has some practical answers.

NOTES

Watch the DVD and record your thoughts here.

Let's turn to the ultimate authority, the Bible, for our starting point. Read individually or as a group:

THE **BACKSTORY**

Now you must put them all away: anger, wrath, malice, slander, and obscene talk from your mouth. Do not lie to one another, seeing that you have put off the old self with its practices and have put on the new self, which is being renewed in knowledge after the image of its creator. … Put on then, as God's chosen ones, holy and beloved, compassionate hearts, kindness, humility, meekness, and patience, bearing with one another and, if one has a complaint against another, forgiving each other; as the Lord has forgiven you, so you also must forgive. And above all these put on love, which binds everything together in perfect harmony. And let the peace of Christ rule in your hearts, to which indeed you were called in one body.

—*Colossians 3: 8-10, 12-15*

You might also want to read:
1 Corinthians 13:7
Ephesians 4:1-3, 32
Philippians 2:5-8
James 5:9

Use the blank lines below the discussion questions to record your initial thoughts, questions, and whatever God might be saying to you through the video, so you can review and reflect on all of this later.

WHAT DO YOU THINK?

1. Does the truth that there are no perfect families give you hope or make you feel hopeless? Why? Why do people pursue the mythical perfect family?

_____

_____

_____

_____

_____

_____

2. Do you think our romantic notions about past family life are mere fiction, or was there indeed something that's been lost? What was your family like when you were growing up?

_____

_____

_____

_____

_____

3. How realistic is the Bible in describing the sort of relationships that should exist between God's people in and outside the home?

_____

_____

_____

_____

_____

4. What are some of the issues that contribute to the ill health of Christian families? In what areas would you like to see your own family improve?

_____

_____

_____

_____

_____

5. What impact can stable but imperfect families have on society? How is your family reaching out to others in the church or community? Tell us about families you know who have adopted children or done something else redemptive.

_____

_____

_____

_____

_____

_____

ONE STEP
I CAN TAKE TOMORROW

Think of and write down at least one practical thing you can do tomorrow as a result of today's session.

WRAP-UP

Thanks for taking the time to go through The Family Project. We hope you found it both informative and inspirational. Now begins the real work! May God bless you as you strive to make your own family all that God intended it to be, and as you reach out together to heal a hurting world.

Remember that for more resources on Christian worldview and God's plan for the family, you can visit **familyproject.com**.

The Family
project™
A Divine Reflection

Resources

Learn about God's design for the family through these transformational resources.

The Family Project Curriculum

A home-based, small-group program consisting of 12 DVD sessions, approximately 60 minutes each, with discussion guides for leaders and participants.

The Family Project will help people understand their personal significance in God's great plan, equipping them to live with an eternal perspective and model God's design for family to their peers, communities, and the world around them.

Additional participants' guides are also available.

The Family Project: How God's Design Reveals His Best for You

This book will help you discover what the Creator of families has in mind for yours—and why there's no substitute for His time-tested design.

The Family Project Devotional

Fifty-two weeks of exploring the Scriptures and growing stronger as a family by learning to love and serve one another.

The Focus on the Family Marriage Series

This series seeks to strengthen relationships between husbands and wives and to enhance their lifelong commitment. As a part of The Family Project resources collection, this 10-book series encourages and equips couples to live out God's design in their marriage.

Adventures in Odyssey: The Ties That Bind

The Ties That Bind contains 12 episodes exploring questions about God's design for marriage and family, loyalty, redemption, commitment and love. It's a collection for your whole family to enjoy and talk about!

To order an extra leader's guide or additional participants' guides, or to see other resources to help your family thrive, please visit **FamilyProject.com**

What you do for family is what they'll do for life.

IT STARTS WITH YOU.

GEN3™ starts with a promise—a commitment to be a thriving family for three generations.

By making intentional decisions every day, you can share a lasting legacy with future generations.

What you do for family is what they'll do for life.

FocusOnTheFamily.com/Gen3

MAKE THE GEN3 PROMISE.